I Dr M. J. Smith,
gyda diolch ~ C.F.

I Doreen a'r teulu,
gyda chariad ~ B.C.

Cyhoeddwyd yn 2021 gan Wasg y Dref Wen,
28 Heol Yr Eglwys, Yr Eglwys Newydd, Caerdydd CF14 2EA,
ffôn 029 20617860.

Cyhoeddiad Saesneg gwreiddiol 2014 gan Simon & Schuster UK Ltd,
1st Floor, 222 Gray's Inn Road, Llundain WC1X 8HB
dan y teitl *Monsters Love Underpants*.

Cyhoeddwyd gyda chymorth ariannol Cyngor Llyfrau Cymru.

Argraffwyd yn China

Angenfilod Mewn Tronsys

Claire Freedman a Ben Cort

Addaswyd gan Gwynne Williams

Mae'r holl angenfilod dwi'n nabod
Yn bethe anghynnes a chas,
Yn HOFFI'ch dychrynu, eich llowcio a'ch llyncu
Gan lyfu eu gwefle â'ch blas.

Ond yr hyn maen nhw'n GARU fwyaf
(Does fawr neb yn gwybod am hyn!)
'Di pob math o dronsys, rhai steilus a siapus
Mewn pob math o liwie ond gwyn!

Ganol nos i lawr yn y dwnjwn
Pam mae'r llygod a'r slumod mewn braw?
Am fod pâr o drôns dur yn creu poene a chur
A gwneud i anghenfil ddweud AAAW!

Mae rhai angenfilod sy'n llenwi
Eu trôns efo slwj gwyrdd a gw.
Ond gwell peidio gofyn be maen nhw'n wneud wedyn –
Mae'n rhywbeth i'w wneud efo pw!

Edrychwch ar beth sydd yn digwydd
Yn yr eira ym mhen ucha'r byd –
Dau leidr hyll blewog 'di dygyd trôns rhewog
I gadw'u penole nhw'n glyd.

Yn y dyfnfor mae rhai sydd yn swancio
Ar ôl ffeindio llong drysor gudd
Mewn tronsys drud drud sy'n berle i gyd.
Maen nhw'n gwisgo rhai newydd bob dydd!

Mae hyd yn oed rhai yn y gofod
Ar blaned anghysbell Ffw-ffenn
Yn chwarae'n ddireidus gêm ceisio dal tronsys
Sy'n disgyn o'r spwtnic uwchben.

A welsoch chi 'rioed yn eich bywyd
Anghenfil mewn helynt fel hyn?
Mae'n rhegi a rhuo a rhegi mwy eto,
"Mae'r blwmin trôns yma'n rhy dynn!"

Nos Sadwrn 'di noson eu disgo.
Â phawb yn eu trôns mwya crand,
Yn aros a chiwio tu allan i'r Ogo'
I gael clywed bechgyn y band.

Pan oedden nhw'n joio a jeifio
A jiglo eu tronsys yn llon,
Ar ganol y bopio dyna'r miwsig yn stopio
A'r troellwr yn gweiddi "HOLD ON!"

"Mae'n rhaid i ni i gyd ruthro adre!
Mae'r haul nawr yn codi uwchben.
Os cawn ni ein dala mewn tronsys mor smala
Bydd pawb yn gwneud sbort am ein pen!"

Nawr os clywch chi sŵn dan eich gwely –
Rhyw siffrwd rhwng sibrwd a si –
Anghenfil sydd yno, un slei, yn straffaglio
Wrth drio eich trôns newydd CHI!

Andrew Brodie Basics

LET'S DO PUNCTUATION

FOR AGES 9–10

with over 100 reward stickers

- Structured punctuation practice
- Regular progress tests
- Matched to the National Curriculum

Andrew Brodie
An imprint of Bloomsbury Publishing Plc

50 Bedford Square
London
WC1B 3DP
UK

1385 Broadway
New York
NY 10018
USA

www.bloomsbury.com

ANDREW BRODIE is a trademark of Bloomsbury Publishing Plc

First published in Great Britain 2017

A catalogue record for this book is available from the British Library.

ISBN
PB: 978-1-4729-4079-7
ePDF: 978-1-4729-4078-0

2 4 6 8 10 9 7 5 3 1

Designed and typeset by Marcus Duck Design
Printed and bound in China by Leo Paper Products

This book is produced using paper that is made from wood grown in managed, sustainable forests. It is natural, renewable and recyclable. The logging and manufacturing processes conform to the environmental regulations of the country of origin.

To find out more about our authors and books visit www.bloomsbury.com. Here you will find extracts, author interviews, details of forthcoming events and the option to sign up for our newsletters.

BLOOMSBURY

Notes for parents

What's in this book

This is the fifth in the series of *Andrew Brodie Basics: Let's Do Punctuation* books. Each book features a clearly structured approach to developing and improving children's knowledge and use of punctuation in their reading and writing.

The National Curriculum states that children in Year 5 should learn appropriate terminology in relation to grammar and punctuation:

- statement
- question
- exclamation
- command
- capital letter
- full stop
- question mark
- exclamation mark
- comma
- bracket
- dash
- apostrophe
- speech marks
- inverted commas
- paragraph.

Note that some schools are instructing their pupils not to use the term 'speech marks' but only to use 'inverted commas'.

They will be learning to create sentences, leaving appropriate spaces between words, and to punctuate their sentences with a capital letter at the start and a full stop, question mark or exclamation mark at the end. They will be using commas, where appropriate, to clarify meaning or to avoid ambiguity, as well as to indicate parenthesis – they will also use brackets or dashes for this purpose. They will be using a capital letter for names of people, places, the days of the week, and the personal pronoun 'I'. They will be learning to use apostrophes to indicate where letters have been omitted or to indicate ownership, including the possessive apostrophe with regular and irregular plurals. They will be punctuating direct speech by using inverted commas (speech marks) correctly.

How you can help

Make sure your child is ready for their punctuation practice and help them to enjoy the activities in this book. If necessary, read the activity through out loud, discussing it so that your child really understands what the writing means. On every page there is a dotted circle where you can add a sticker to reward your child for working really hard.

The answer section

The answer section at the end of this book can be a useful teaching tool: ask your child to compare their responses to the ones shown. Their answers will not be identical but should include similar information. If your child has made mistakes, they can learn from these and do better next time. Remember that sometimes progress will seem very slow but at other times it can be surprisingly rapid.

Most importantly, enjoy the experience of working with your child. Together you can share the excitement of learning.

Look out for...

Rufus the Raccoon, who may tell your child what to focus on when working on the page.

Brodie's Brain Boosters, which feature quick extra activities designed to make your child think, using the skills and knowledge they already have. Can your child talk about their experiences using appropriate and interesting vocabulary? Can they then write well-punctuated sentences that give the information clearly?

Contents

Capital letters and full stops

Every sentence starts with a capital letter.

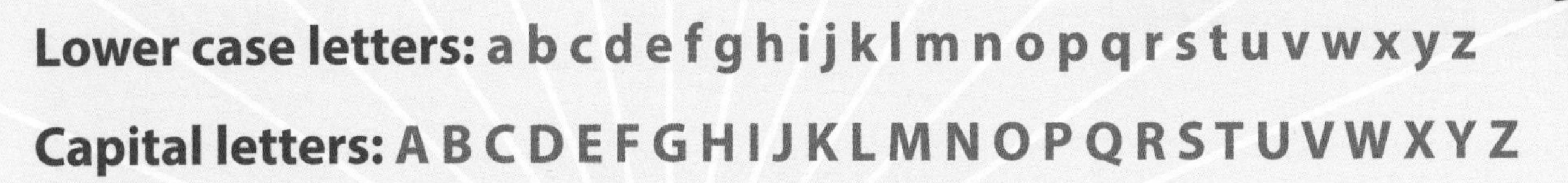

Lower case letters: a b c d e f g h i j k l m n o p q r s t u v w x y z

Capital letters: A B C D E F G H I J K L M N O P Q R S T U V W X Y Z

Every sentence starts with a capital letter.

Most sentences end with a full stop.

Write the following sentences correctly.

the audience went quiet when the curtains opened

____

suddenly the first actor appeared in a puff of smoke

____

everyone clapped loudly even though she had not said a word

____

there was great surprise when she started singing

____

the song ended with an extremely high note

____

the audience leapt to their feet in great excitement

____

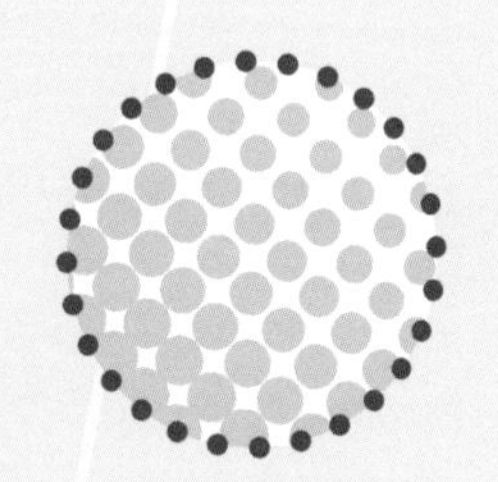

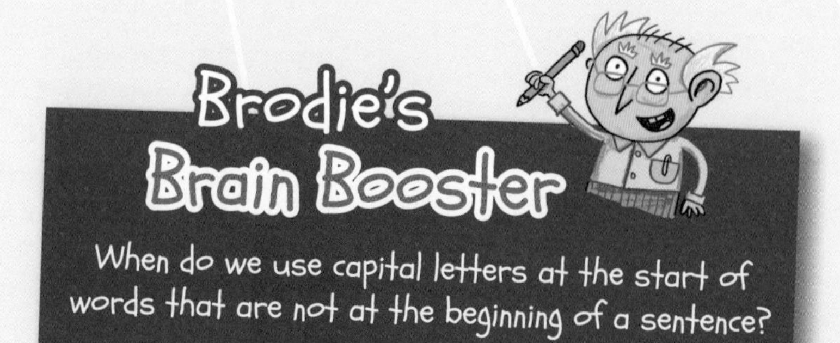

Brodie's
Brain Booster
When do we use capital letters at the start of words that are not at the beginning of a sentence?

Capital letters for names, days, months and titles

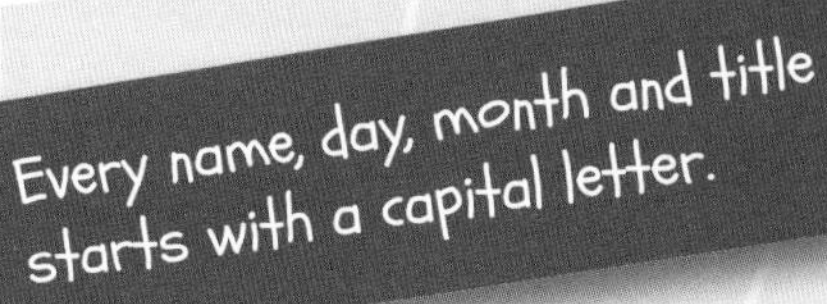

Every name, day, month and title starts with a capital letter.

Write the following sentences correctly.

my aunt has done a lot of travelling this year

____

she went to france in february and china in march

____

she was at home for easter but then went to america in may

____

she visited my uncle william in june

____

she told me that she watched a film called moana when she was on the plane

____

____

i am glad she is at home now but on monday she is going to germany until friday

____

____

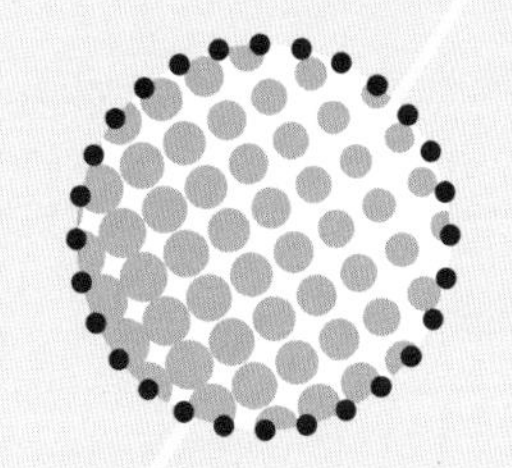

Questions and answers

Every question sentence ends with a question mark.

Every sentence starts with a capital letter.

Most sentences end with a full stop, but some end with a question mark or an exclamation mark.

Write the following sentences correctly. Some of them are questions and some are answers.

what is the highest mountain in the world

____

the highest mountain in the world is mount everest

____

what is the biggest ocean in the world

____

the biggest ocean is the pacific ocean

____

what is the longest river in the world

____

some people think that the longest river in the world is the amazon river and some people think it is the river nile

____

____

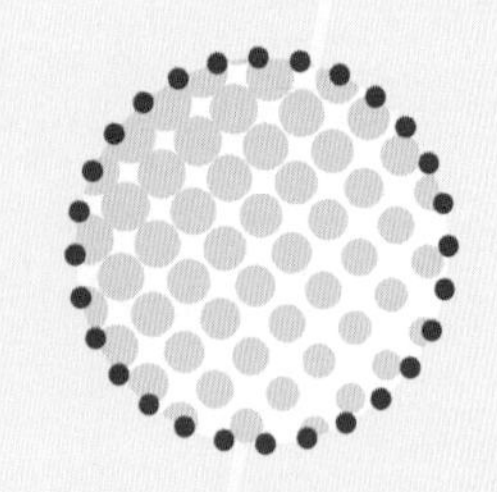

Brodie's Brain Booster

Find information about the Amazon River and the River Nile. Why do people disagree about which is longer?

Creating questions

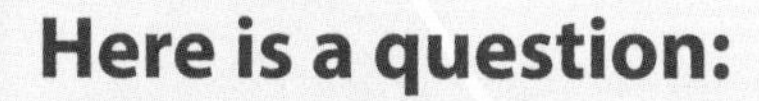

Don't forget capital letters, full stops and question marks.

Here is a question:

What is the biggest lake in the United Kingdom?

Here is the answer:

The lake with the largest area is Lough Neagh in Northern Ireland but the lake with the biggest volume of water is Loch Ness in Scotland.

Can you create three questions about England, Northern Ireland, Scotland or Wales?

1 ______________________________

____

____

2 ______________________________

____

____

3 ______________________________

____

____

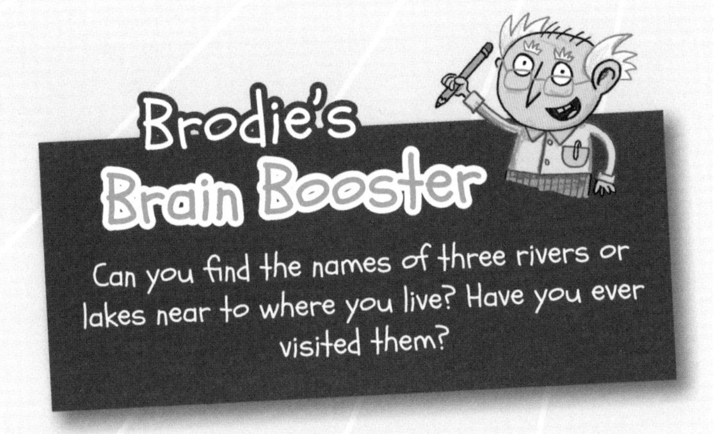

Brodie's
Brain Booster
Can you find the names of three rivers or lakes near to where you live? Have you ever visited them?

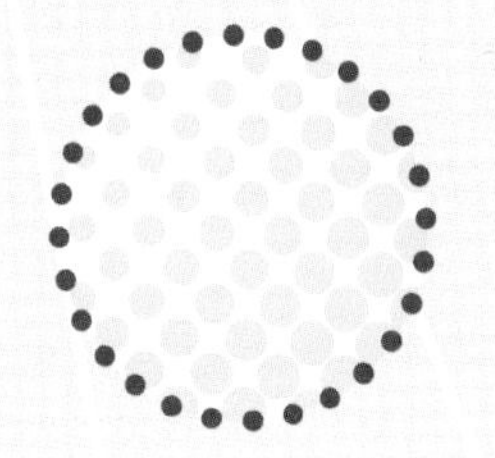

Finding answers

Don't forget to write your answers as full sentences.

Can you find the answers to the questions you wrote on page 7?

1. ______________________________

____

____

2. ______________________________

____

____

3. ______________________________

____

____

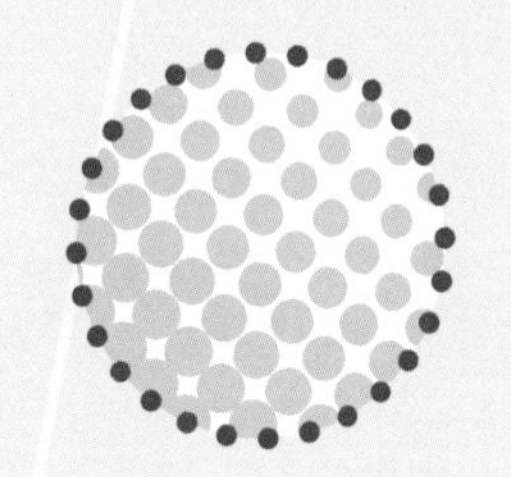

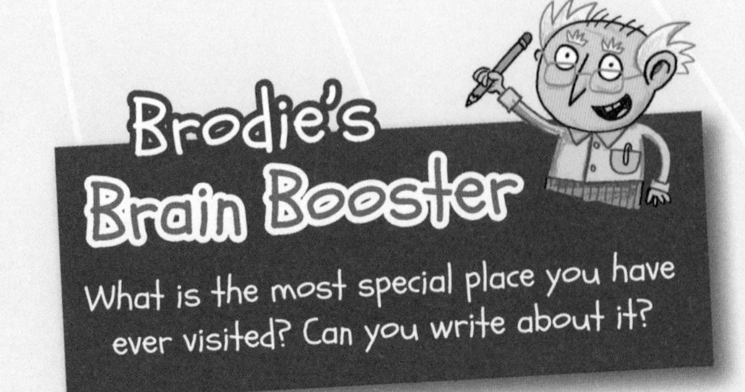

Brodie's
Brain Booster
What is the most special place you have ever visited? Can you write about it?

Using question marks

Can you work out where the question marks go?

Some of the sentences below should end with question marks. Put a tick next to each sentence that must end with a question mark.

Tick six.

What time is the bus coming ☐

What a long journey this is ☐

Ask your friend to go to the park with you ☐

How many days are there until Christmas ☐

Where is the remote control ☐

How funny that film was ☐

What would you like for your birthday ☐

When are you going on holiday ☐

Why did the chicken cross the road ☐

What a mess the dog has made ☐

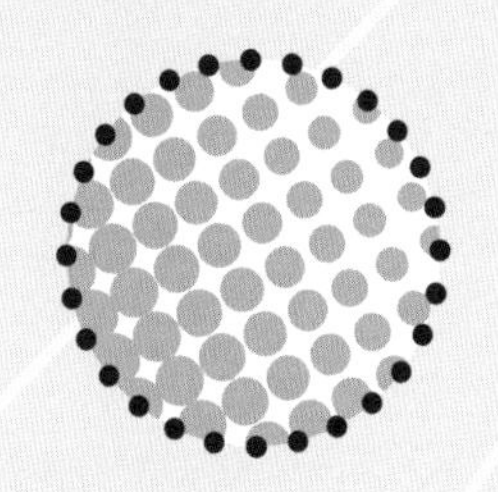

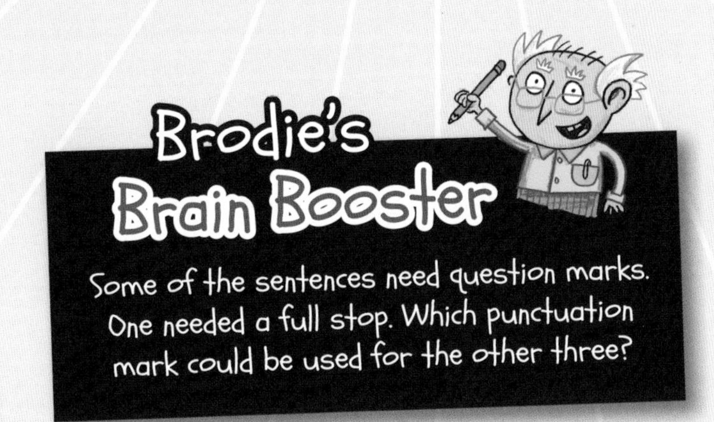

Brodie's Brain Booster
Some of the sentences need question marks. One needed a full stop. Which punctuation mark could be used for the other three?

The sentences below have been written incorrectly. Write them out correctly.

where did you go at the weekend

____

i went to london and took a boat ride on the river thames

____

when are you going there again

____

we hope to go back in october

____

i am going to london on wednesday to see a show

____

what show are you going to see

____

school of rock

____

One of the sentences below should end with a question mark. Put a tick by the sentence that must end with a question mark.

	Tick one.
Ask the teacher if you get stuck	☐
What is the longest river in the world	☐
How beautiful the snow looks	☐
I haven't found my book yet	☐

Exclamation marks

Exclamation marks are used to show strong feelings.

Zoom! Wow! Brilliant! Oh no!

Each of the following sentences could be an exclamation. Write the sentences correctly.

what a great day for a swim

____

how scary that film was

____

what a mess the dog has made

____

i am so excited

____

this tastes delicious

____

Brodie's Brain Booster

Look in the book you are reading. Can you find any exclamations? Why do you think the author used an exclamation mark?

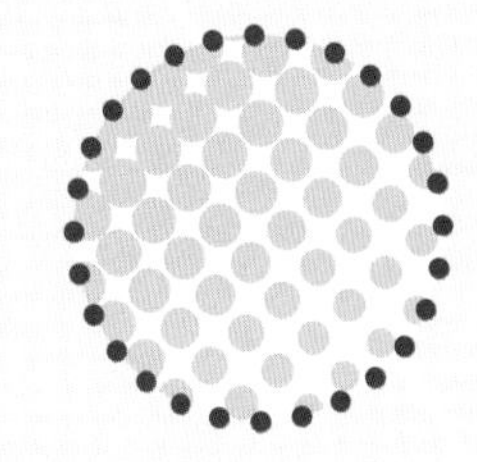

Apostrophes

Apostrophes are used for two main purposes.

Apostrophes can be used to shorten words where letters have been missed out. Look:

we have  **we've**

This is an apostrophe.

The letters h and a in the word have have been omitted from we have to make the contracted form we've.

Write the contracted form of the underlined words in the boxes. It could help to read the words out loud.

I did not see the tree that had fallen across the road until it was too late.

We were not able to go to the zoo yesterday.

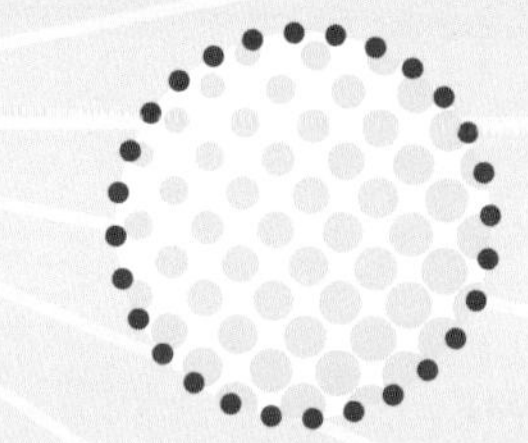

I have not seen my cat today.

We should have asked the way to the station.

I think I know what is wrong with the car.

Do you know what the words **omission** and **contracted** mean?

I cannot get the car to start.

Apostrophes for omissions

Letters have been omitted from some words in the sentences below. Write the long form of the underlined words in full, in the boxes.

I would've liked the show last night.

I couldn't find my shoes this morning.

The train went through the station but didn't stop.

The joke wasn't very funny really.

The grass doesn't grow very much in the winter so I won't need to cut it.

I can't see the bird in the tree but I know it's there.

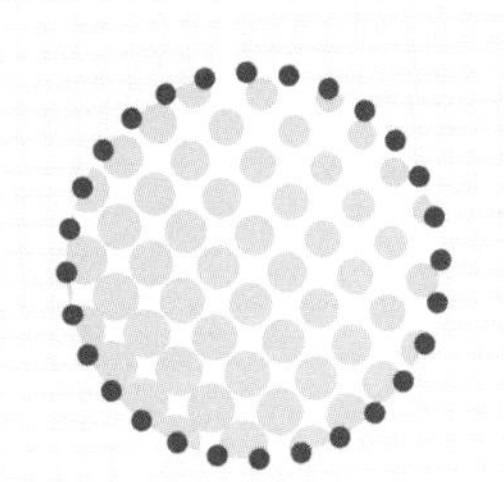

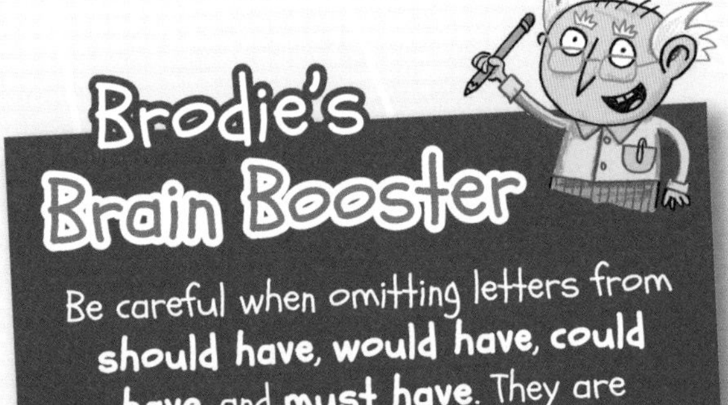

Brodie's
Brain Booster
Be careful when omitting letters from should have, would have, could have and must have. They are contracted to should've, would've, could've and must've not should of, would of, could of or must of.

Possessive apostrophes

We also use apostrophes to show that someone owns something.

Look at this example:

My teacher's car has broken down.

The car belongs to the teacher. It is her possession.
We call the apostrophe a possessive apostrophe.

Each sentence below needs a possessive apostrophe.
Rewrite each sentence correctly.

the dogs lead is hanging on the hook

____

i was surprised how long the mouses tail was

____

i picked up amys book when she dropped it on the floor

____

she told me it was teds book not hers

____

i put the book on teds desk

____

Brodie's Brain Booster
Look in the book you are reading. Can you find any possessive apostrophes?

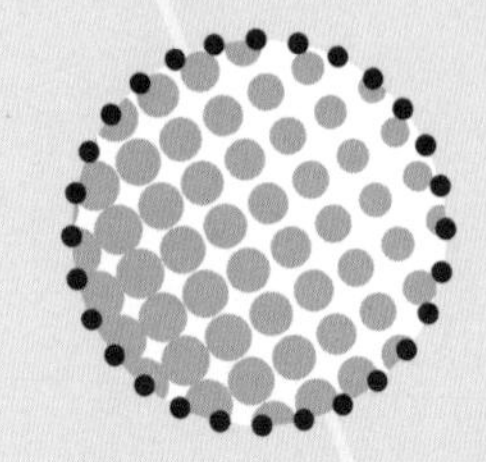

Possessive apostrophes with plurals

We can use possessive apostrophes when there is more than one owner.

Look at this example:

The men's shoes are on display at the very back of the shop.

We can tell that the shoes are for more than one man. The sentence implies that they are for sale in a shop. The shoes are for the men, which is a plural word. The apostrophe is placed after the word men.

Each sentence below needs a possessive apostrophe. Rewrite each sentence correctly.

the womens choir performed at the royal albert hall

---

maria and luke went to the childrens party

Now look at these plural words:

boys

With these words, the apostrophe goes after the whole word. Look at this example:

The dogs' leads are hanging on the hooks.

We can tell that the leads are for more than one dog. The leads are for the dogs, which is a plural word. The apostrophe is placed after the word dogs.

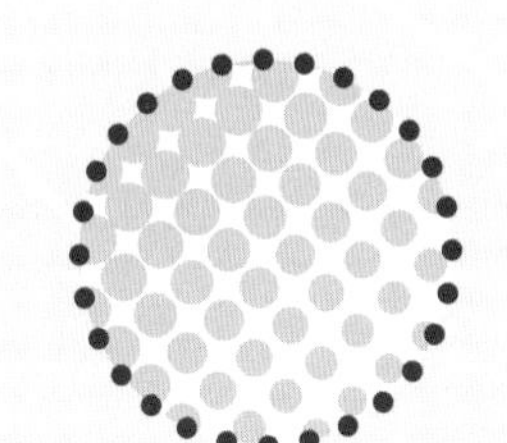

Each sentence below needs a possessive apostrophe. Rewrite each sentence correctly.

the girls football team won the whole tournament

---

the boys football team came second

Can you spot which sentences are correct?

Which sentence uses an apostrophe correctly?

Tick one.

The ladies netball teams' were ready for the tournament. ☐

The ladies netball team's were ready for the tournament. ☐

The ladies' netball teams were ready for the tournament. ☐

The ladie's netball teams were ready for the tournament. ☐

Write a sentence about the bikes belonging to the girls.

____

____

Write a sentence about the books belonging to the boys.

____

____

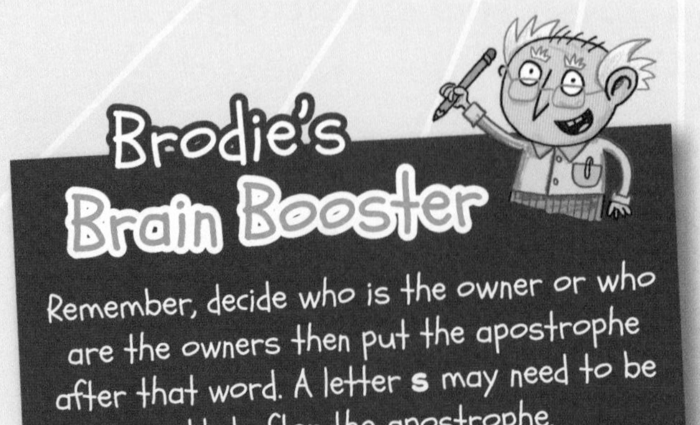

Remember, decide who is the owner or who are the owners then put the apostrophe after that word. A letter **s** may need to be added after the apostrophe.

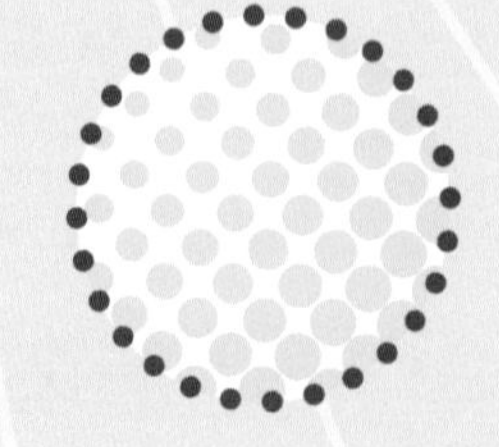

Which sentence uses an apostrophe correctly? **Tick one.**

My mums' car is bright yellow but the seats are blue. ☐

My mums' car is bright yellow but the seats are blue. ☐

My mum's car is bright yellow but the seats are blue. ☐

My mums' car is bright yellow but the seats' are blue. ☐

Each sentence below needs a possessive apostrophe. Rewrite each sentence correctly.

The dogs blanket fell on the floor. (one dog)

____

I watched Amys paper aeroplane as it flew across the playground.

____

All the other childrens aeroplanes didn't get very far.

____

Some of the animals cages are brightly coloured.

____

We added an extra tunnel to our hamsters cage. (one hamster)

____

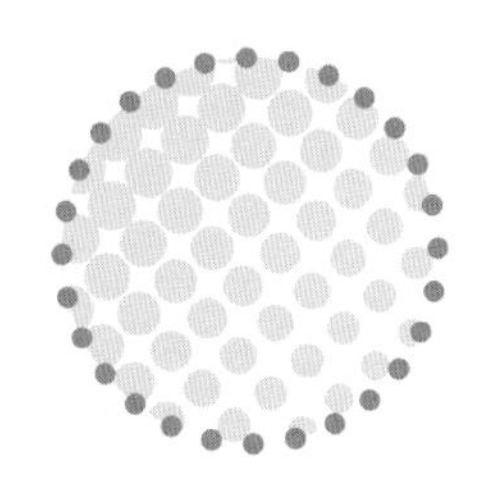

Inverted commas

Inverted commas are sometimes called speech marks.

What would you like to eat?
A big bar of chocolate please!

Mum asked a question and Tom replied. We can show their short conversation as direct speech. For direct speech, we need speech marks, which are sometimes called inverted commas.

"What would you like to eat?" asked Mum.

"A big bar of chocolate please!" replied Tom.

Here is some more of their conversation, but this time the punctuation is missing. Write it out with the correct punctuation.

that is not what i meant said mum i would really like a bar of chocolate said tom so would i said mum

____

____

____

____

Brodie's Brain Booster

Look in the book you are reading. Can you find any inverted commas? Are they single inverted commas? 'Hello.' Or are they double inverted commas? "Hello."

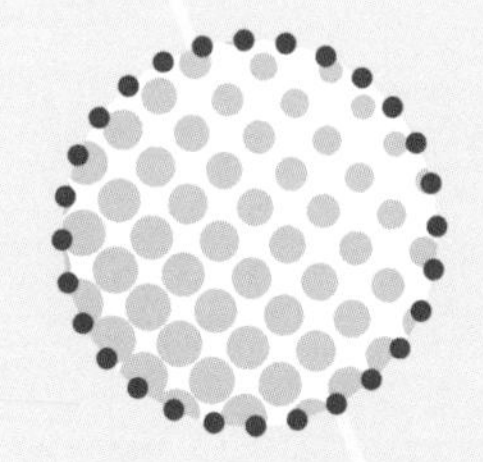

Direct speech

Do you know the rules for punctuating speech?

Rules for punctuating direct speech:

Inverted commas are written before and after the words spoken.	There is always a comma, a question mark, an exclamation mark or a full stop before the closing speech marks.	A new line is started when a different person speaks.

Rewrite the following passage with the correct punctuation.

when will my new book arrive asked ted it should come today replied lucy thank you for ordering it for me said ted well it is your birthday said lucy

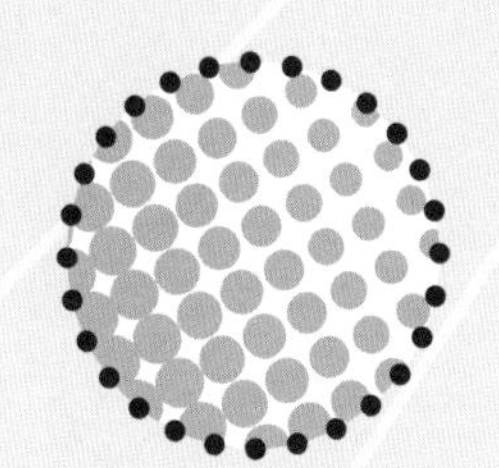

Brodie's Brain Booster
When we are writing direct speech, we use verbs such as **said, asked, replied, shouted, mumbled, whispered.**

How many speech verbs can you think of?

Here are some verbs we use for speech:

said | asked | replied | shouted | mumbled

Can you think of some more speech verbs? Write them below. Use your reading book to help you if you're not sure.

______________________ ______________________

______________________ ______________________

______________________ ______________________

Rewrite the following short passage, punctuating it correctly.

do you want to play football asked molly that would be good but we cant said elliott why not said molly because we havent got a ball answered elliott

____

____

____

____

____

____

Brodie's Brain Booster

Conversations are sometimes written as a play script.

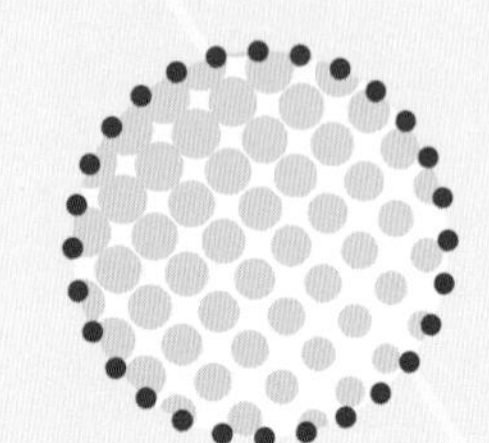

Play script

Can you continue the script?

Read this short script.

Eli Have you got any sweets?

Piotr Yes, I've got loads.

Eli Do you want to share them?

Piotr Not really.

Did you notice that we write the name of the speaker before we write what they say? Write a few more lines of the script. Will Piotr share his sweets with Eli? You can decide.

____

____

____

____

____

____

____

____

Brodie's Brain Booster

Have you ever acted in a play? Can you still remember your lines?

Changing a play script to direct speech

Do you remember the rules for writing direct speech?

Read the script that you extended on page 21. Write it out as direct speech. Here is a reminder of the rules:

Inverted commas are written before and after the words spoken.	There is always a comma, a question mark, an exclamation mark or a full stop before the closing speech marks.	A new line is started when a different person speaks.

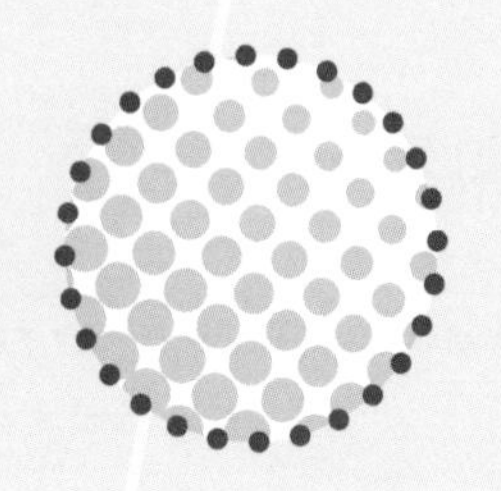

Brodie's Brain Booster

Sometimes we don't need a speech verb to work out who is speaking. Look in the book you are reading. Can you find a place where someone speaks but no speech verb is shown?

Direct speech again

Sometimes we don't need a speech verb.

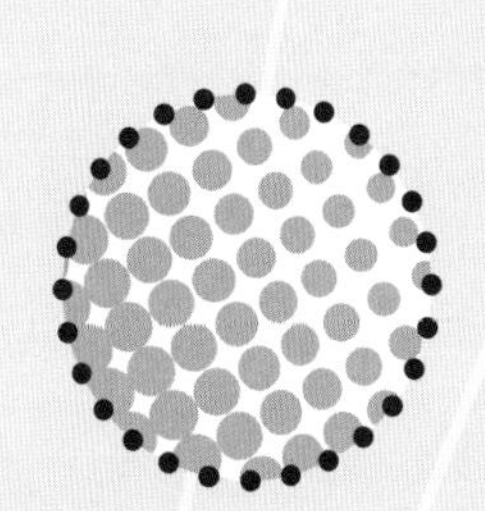

"What flavour is your ice cream?" asked the boy.

"Chocolate."

It is easy to tell from the short passage of writing that the girl's ice cream was chocolate flavoured. There was no need to write replied the girl.

Read the short passage below and try to work out who is speaking. Rewrite the passage, using the correct punctuation.

what is your favourite flavour asked karen i think its vanilla replied oliver mine is mint choc chip said karen i dont like that one said oliver the one i dont like is fudge said karen why not asked oliver its too sweet

Brodie's Brain Booster

Did you notice that some apostrophes were needed when you punctuated the passage?

Change the play script below to direct speech.

Claire This maths is easy.

Harley It may be for you but I'm finding it quite difficult.

Claire Can I help you?

Harley Can you show me how to change this fraction to a decimal?

Claire You know that a half is the same as five tenths, don't you?

Harley So a half must be zero point five!

Rewrite the passage below, punctuating it correctly.

can you play a musical instrument asked molly i can play the guitar replied fynn i can play the piano said molly we could play a duet said fynn what song do you want to play asked molly you choose

Well Done
Excellent
Great Work
Fantastic
FAB
Good Job
Keep It Up
Magnificent
Brilliant Work
SUPER
Well Done
Excellent
Great Work
Fantastic
FAB
Good Job
Keep It Up
Magnificent
Brilliant Work
SUPER
Well Done
Excellent
Great Work
Fantastic
FAB
Good Job
Keep It Up
Magnificent
Brilliant Work
SUPER
Well Done
Excellent
Great Work
Fantastic
FAB

Well Done
Excellent
Great Work
Fantastic
FAB
!
?
Good Job
Keep It Up
Magnificent
Brilliant Work
SUPER
Well Done
Excellent
Great Work
Fantastic
FAB
!
?
Good Job
Keep It Up
Magnificent
Brilliant Work
SUPER
Well Done
Excellent
Great Work
Fantastic
FAB
!
?
Good Job
Keep It Up
Magnificent
Brilliant Work
SUPER
Well Done
Excellent
Great Work
Fantastic
FAB

We can use commas to show exactly what we mean.

Look at the sentences below.

"Shall we go and ask, Lily?" said Maddie.

"Shall we go and ask Lily?" said Maddie.

In the first sentence the comma indicates that we should pause slightly. We can tell that Maddie is asking Lily whether they should both go and ask someone else a question.

In the second sentence, there is no comma. Maddie is asking someone else whether they should both go and ask Lily a question.

Here is another example of a pair of sentences meaning different things:

"Shall we eat George?" said Mum.

"Shall we eat, George?" said Mum.

What is wrong with the first of these two sentences?

____

____

What did Mum mean really, as shown in the second sentence?

____

____

Brodie's
Brain Booster
Look in the book you are reading. How many commas can you find on the first page?

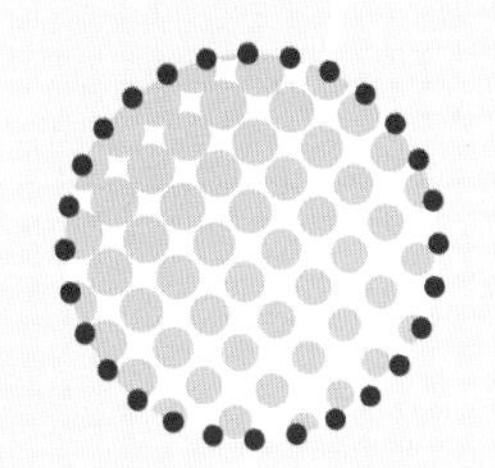

Commas after introductory phrases

Commas are often used after introductory phrases.

Look at these examples:

Of course, the food tasted better than it looked.

Finally, the show came to an end and we could all go home.

In March, my relatives are coming to visit.

Rewrite the sentences below, using commas in appropriate places. Each sentence only needs one comma.

once upon a time the duke of york climbed up a hill

early this morning the weather was quite good

before we start would you like a cup of tea

at that moment the sun appeared from behind a cloud

after the rain the grass looked fresh and green

next month i am going to start rugby lessons

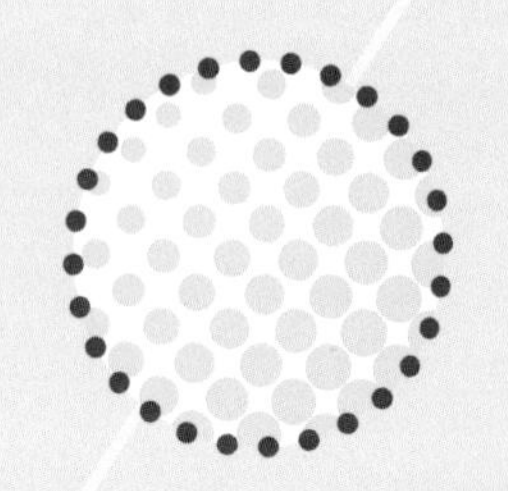

Brodie's
Brain Booster
Commas are used to separate items in a list.

Commas in lists

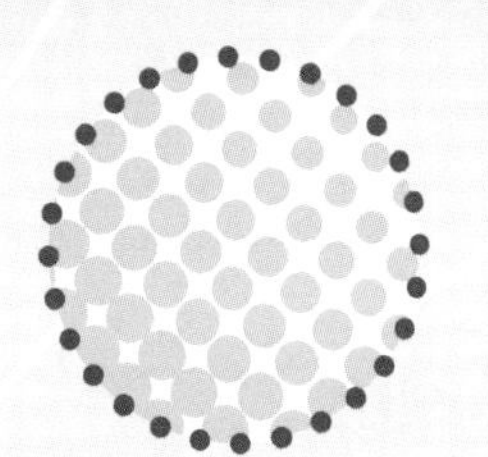

Commas can be used to separate items in a list.

Look at this example:

My favourite vegetables are carrots, peas and sweetcorn.

In the list of vegetables, there were three items: carrots peas sweetcorn. Did you notice that there was only one comma? The comma and the word and are used to separate the items.

Look at another example:

My sister studies maths, English, science, art, PE, French and RE.

There were seven items in the list so there were five commas and the word and.

Rewrite the following sentences, punctuating them correctly.

we bought new trousers socks shirts and jackets ready for our winter holiday

____

____

my mum has been to france spain portugal italy and germany for her work

____

____

there are lots of oak trees in the forest but there are also some beech ash birch and sycamore trees

____

____

the teacher said i should have pens pencils an eraser a pencil sharpener and a protractor in my pencil case

____

____

Commas to separate clauses

Look at this example:

My favourite food, apart from chocolate, is fish and chips.

The phrase apart from chocolate is not giving essential information. It is giving extra information to make the sentence more interesting. The sentence could have just been: My favourite food is fish and chips. To separate the extra information, it is written between commas.

Rewrite the following sentences with correct punctuation.

the bike shop the one near the railway station sells a bike in every colour

____

____

i forgot my book which i only bought yesterday so i had to go back for it

____

____

the tent a green one was big enough to make a huge den

____

____

we caught the train at Victoria which is our most convenient station and reached the seaside in less than an hour and a half

____

____

Brodie's Brain Booster
Commas that separate out an extra piece of information are sometimes called bracketing commas.

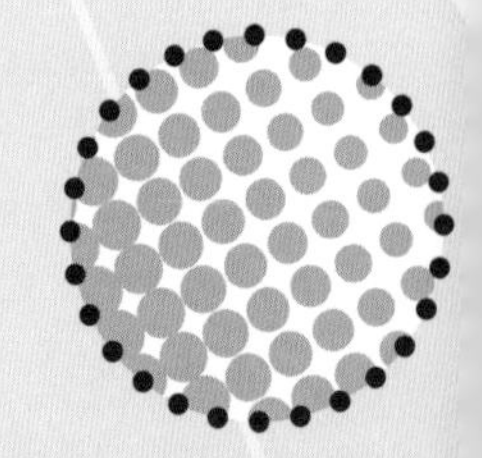

More commas to separate clauses

Commas can be used to separate clauses.

Look at this example:

When I'm older, if what my mum says is true, I'll be a good driver.

The phrase if what my mum says is true is giving extra information so it is written between a pair of commas.

Rewrite the following sentences but add extra information to each one. Use a pair of commas to separate out the extra information in each of your sentences.

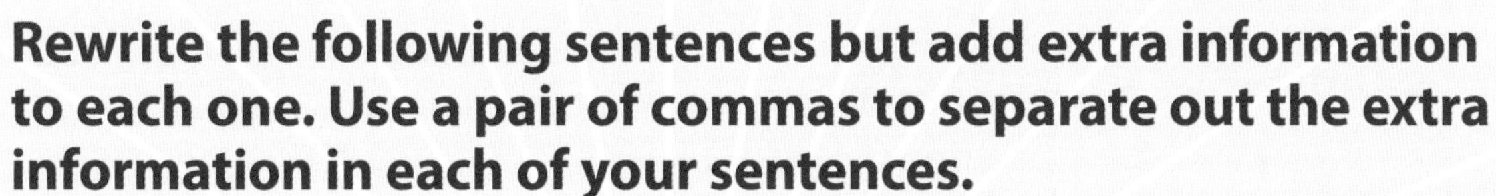

i got off my bike and went into the shop to buy some sweets

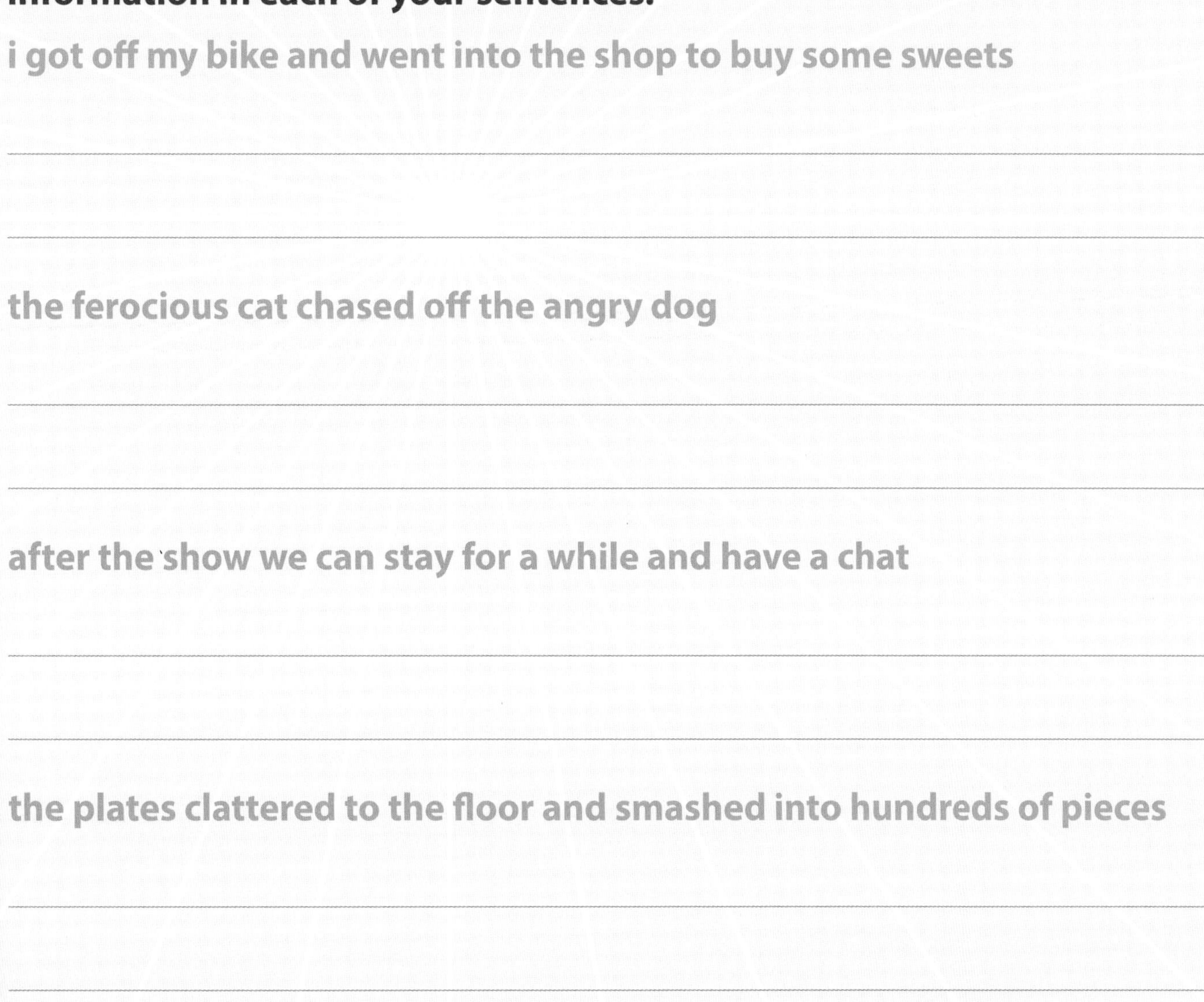

the ferocious cat chased off the angry dog

after the show we can stay for a while and have a chat

the plates clattered to the floor and smashed into hundreds of pieces

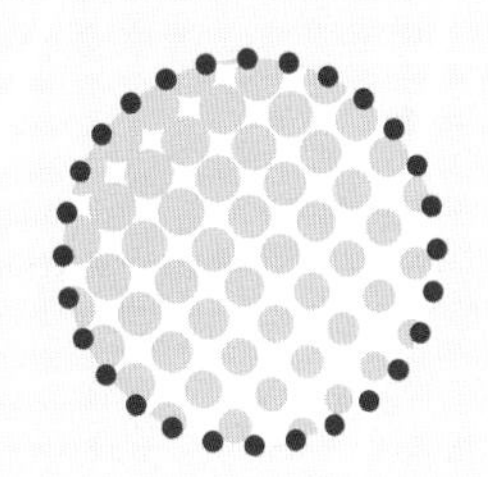

Brodie's
Brain Booster
Look in the book you are reading. Can you find any bracketing commas?

Speech marks

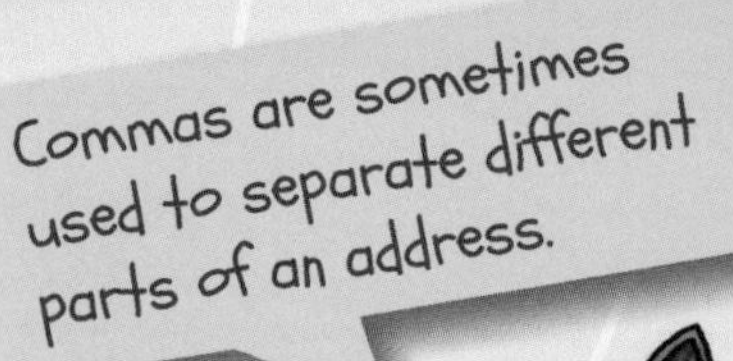

Here is the Prime Minister's address, written with commas and without commas:

The Prime Minister, 10 Downing Street, London SW1A 2AA	The Prime Minister 10 Downing Street London SW1A 2AA

Here is another example of an address:

Mrs A Hardy, Old Barn Cottage, Westfield Road, Charton, Derbyshire DB7 3AB	Mrs A Hardy Old Barn Cottage Westfield Road Charton Derbyshire DB7 3AB

What do you notice about where commas are used and where they are not used?

Most people don't use commas in addresses any more. Write your address with commas and without commas. Don't forget the capital letters.

Brodie's
Brain Booster
Look at addresses on envelopes. Do the addresses have commas?

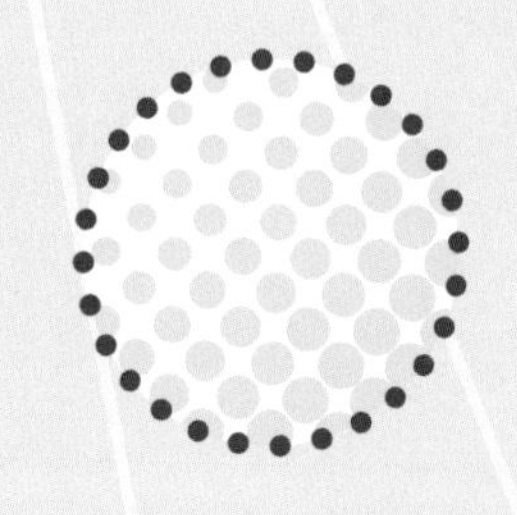

Put a tick next to the sentence that shows Joe is talking to Poppy. **Tick one.**

"I'm stuck on my maths so I'm going to ask, Poppy," said Joe. ☐

"I'm stuck on my maths so I'm going to ask Poppy," said Joe. ☐

Which sentence has been punctuated correctly? **Tick one.**

After, going for a swim we had a boat trip to the island. ☐

After going for a swim we had a boat trip, to the island. ☐

After going for a swim, we had a boat trip to the island. ☐

After going for a swim we had, a boat trip to the island. ☐

Which sentence has been punctuated correctly? **Tick one.**

The new house built last year, can be described as an eco-house. ☐

The new house, built last year, can be described as an eco-house. ☐

The new house built last year can be described, as an eco-house. ☐

The new house, built last year can be described as an eco-house. ☐

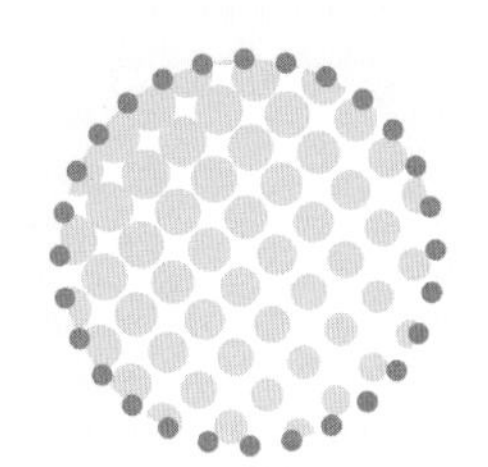

Brackets

I have already mentioned bracketing commas.

Brackets can be used to enclose extra information in a sentence. Sometimes we choose to use commas and sometimes we choose to use brackets. You have the choice.

Look at these examples:

The computer (a new model) is very fast.

The computer, which is a new model, is very fast.

Both sentences give us the same information that the computer is very fast and both have the extra information about when the model of the computer.

The sentences could also be written like this:

The computer, a new model, is very fast.

The computer (which is a new model) is very fast.

Write a sentence about a superhero who can fly a long way without getting tired. Add extra information that the superhero mostly eats bananas. You can choose whether to use brackets or commas.

Brodie's Brain Booster
Look in your reading book. Can you find any brackets?

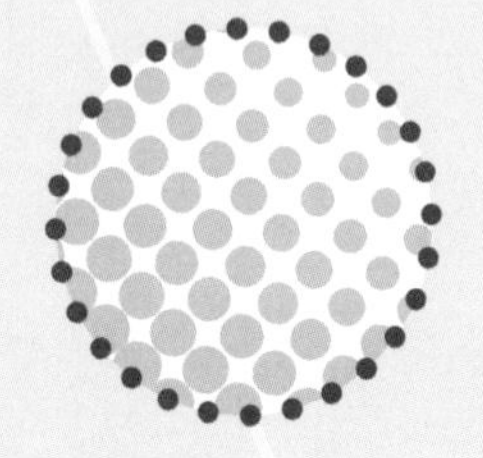

Dashes in pairs

Dashes can sometimes be used instead of brackets.

Dashes can also be used to enclose extra information in a sentence. Sometimes we choose to use commas, sometimes we choose to use brackets and sometimes we choose to use dashes. You have the choice.

Look at this example:

The picture was good – brilliant, in fact – so the teacher put it in the centre of the display.

Did you notice that there is a comma after the word brilliant, so it would not be good to use bracketing commas in this sentence. There would be too many commas. The dashes are a good choice.

Rewrite the sentences below, using dashes in appropriate places.

The tree house high above the ground gave a great vantage point to see who was approaching.

The superhero travelling faster than the speed of sound shot across the night sky.

Write a sentence of your own using a pair of dashes to give extra information.

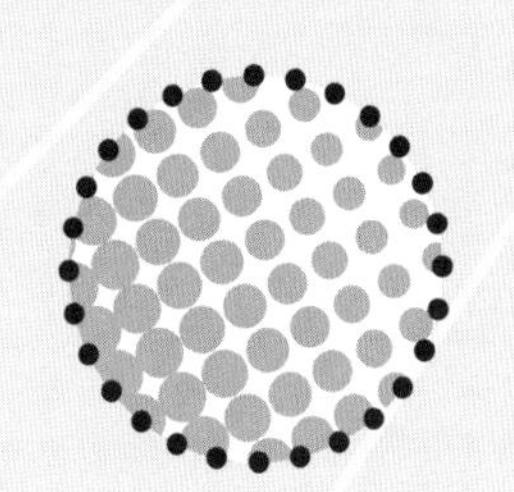

Brodie's
Brain Booster
Look in your reading book. Can you find any dashes used in a similar way to brackets or bracketing commas?

Dashes on their own

Dashes are sometimes used on their own.

Dashes are often used to introduce information at the end of a sentence.

Look at this sentence, which does not include a dash:

The box full of presents was a complete surprise.

Now look at this example:

The box full of presents – a complete surprise.

In the second example, the dash has been used to emphasise what the surprise was. Notice how the word was has been removed.

Rewrite the sentences below. Use a dash in an appropriate place in each one. There is no need to remove any words.

I was thrilled when the experiment was successful hooray!

____

____

Be careful of that tree I've just planted it.

____

____

Put the television on my friend is starring in a new show.

____

____

Hurry up and get the tomato ketchup my chips are getting cold.

____

____

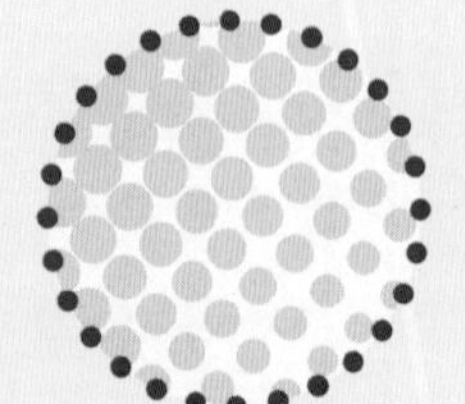

Dashes to replace words

Dashes can be used in place of some words.

Look at this sentence:

I looked through the binoculars but could see nothing but blue sky.

Now look at this sentence:

I looked through the binoculars – nothing but blue sky.

The dash emphasises that the viewer cannot see what he or she is searching for.

Here is another example:

I phoned the Mike about the football match on Saturday but there was no answer.

I phoned the Mike about the football match on Saturday – no answer.

Rewrite the sentences below. Use a dash in an appropriate place to shorten them into one sentence.

We parked our scooters at the bottom of the hill. This was a very handy spot.

Brodie's
Brain Booster
Look in your reading book. Can you find any dashes used to miss out words?

More dashes to replace words

Dashes can be used in place of some words.

Look at this sentence:

Here, the dash is being used to imply that there is a problem. Mum is hesitating rather than saying something negative about the dog.

Write the conversation that the mother and daughter could have about the dog.

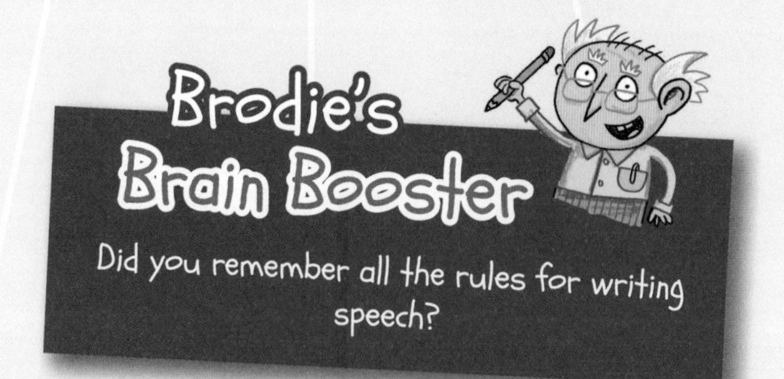

Brodie's Brain Booster
Did you remember all the rules for writing speech?

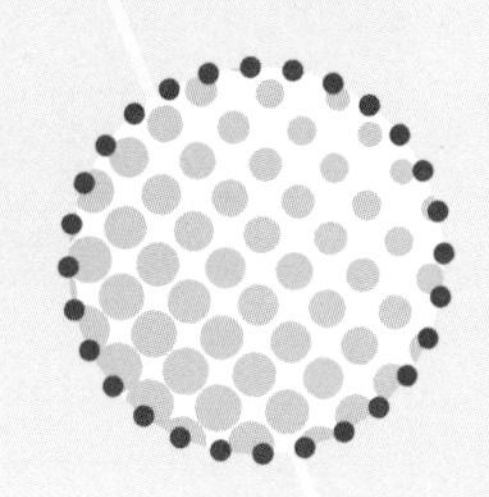

Commas, brackets and dashes

Although there are rules for punctuation, you also have some choices to make. You can decide when to use commas, when to use brackets and when to use dashes.

Rewrite the sentences below, using commas, brackets or dashes where appropriate.

It was raining pouring down so we left the beach early.

The book which was written in 2017 is all about a boy who shrinks.

I went to the bookshop it had closed early.

The chocolate was delicious it tasted of raspberries.

The school opened in 1878 is still very important in the village.

The new house very modern in appearance has a flat roof.

Progress Test 5

Rewrite the sentences below, using commas, brackets or dashes where appropriate.

The sky was bright blue just a few clouds and we could feel the warmth from the sun.

I jumped on my bike which is a mountain bike and raced to the end of the field.

We ate all the food delicious then got back on the trampolines.

Rewrite the sentences below. Use a dash in an appropriate place to shorten them into one sentence.

The sun shone all day and the sea was warm. It was a fantastic day at the beach.

Rewrite the sentence below. Use a dash in an appropriate place.

The work was much easier than I expected I'm beginning to like maths.

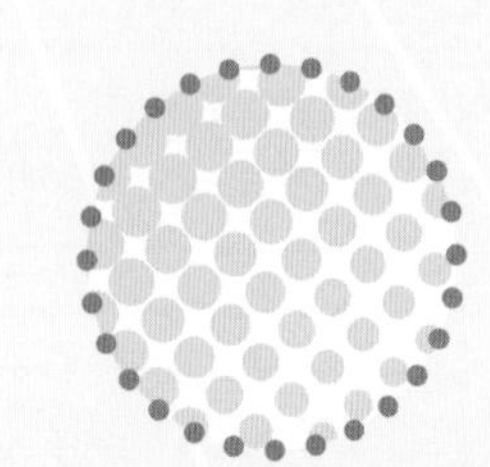

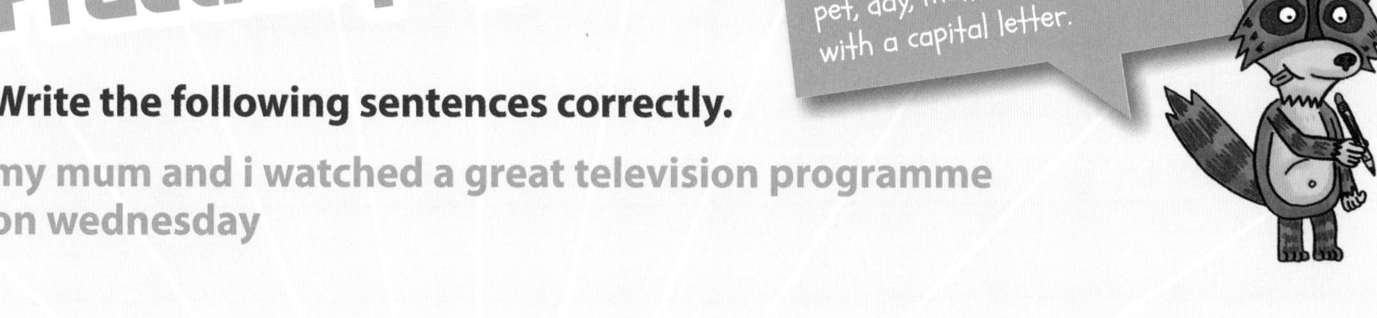

Write the following sentences correctly.

my mum and i watched a great television programme on wednesday

____

it was all about a desert in africa

____

it is hot there all year round even in january

____

there are lots of different animals there

____

they are adapted to cope with the hot conditions

____

i told my teacher mrs watkins all about the programme

____

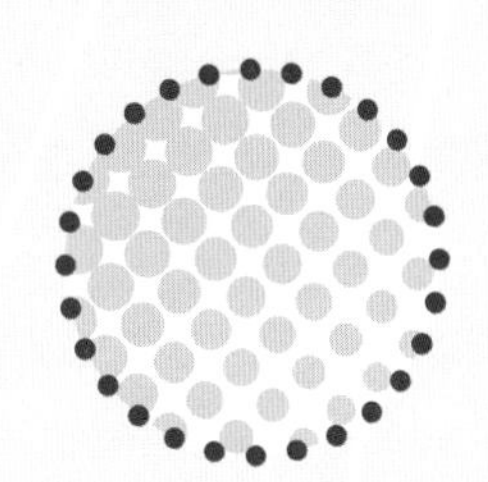

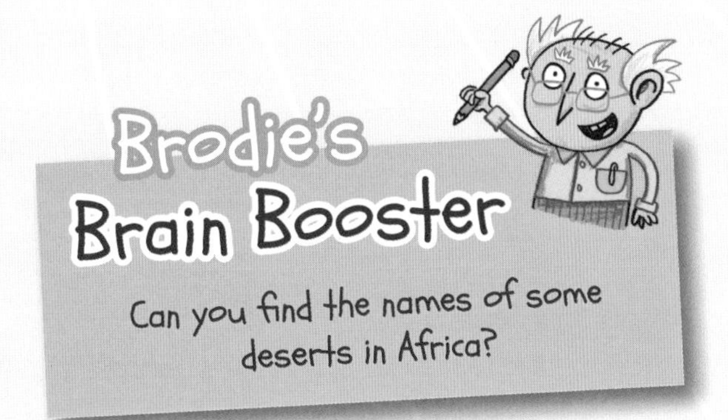

Brodie's
Brain Booster
Can you find the names of some deserts in Africa?

Practice pages

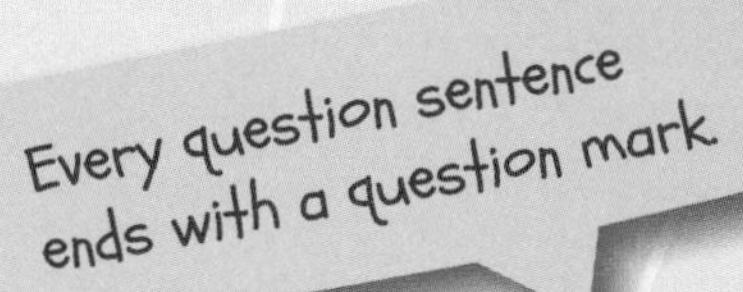

Every sentence starts with a capital letter.

Most sentences end with a full stop but some end with a question mark or an exclamation mark.

Write the following sentences correctly. Some of them are questions and some are answers.

what is the biggest hot desert in the world

___

the biggest hot desert in the world is the sahara desert

___

where is the sahara desert

___

the sahara desert is in north africa

___

what is the biggest cold desert in the world

___

the biggest cold desert is antarctica

___

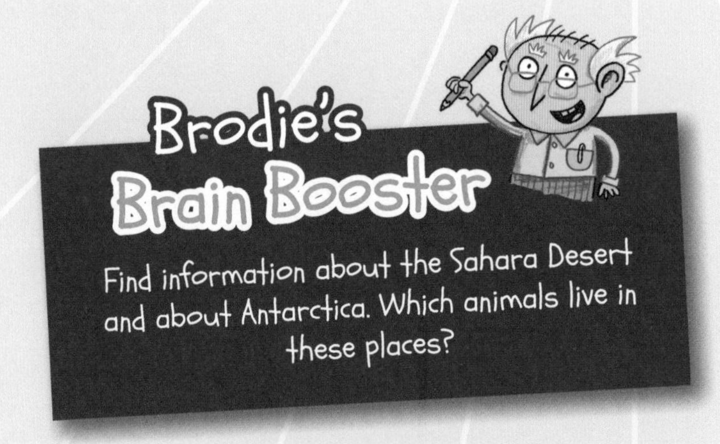

Brodie's Brain Booster
Find information about the Sahara Desert and about Antarctica. Which animals live in these places?

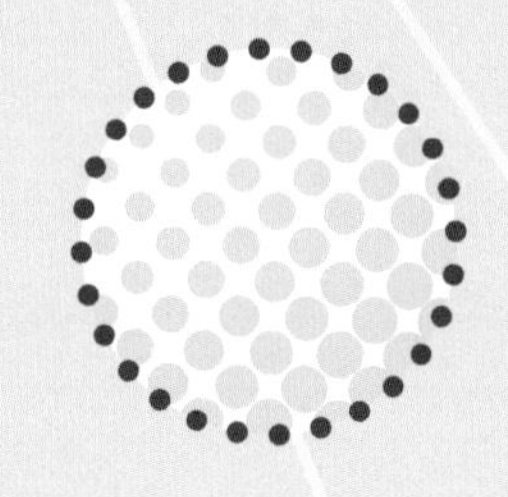

Practice pages

Apostrophes can be used to shorten words where letters are missed out and they can be used to show possession or ownership.

Rewrite the sentences below, inserting apostrophes in appropriate places.

dad cant find his phone so hes using mums

____

i found robs book which hed left in the childminders car

____

i wouldve liked to call olivia yesterday but she was away

____

i havent seen hollys latest picture but i know itll be good because shes a great artist

____

____

it takes a long time to cut the lawn as the gardens so big

____

weve brought lots of childrens toys for the toddlers to play with

____

Brodie's Brain Booster
Keep a look out for apostrophes that are used incorrectly. Lots of adults make mistakes with apostrophes!

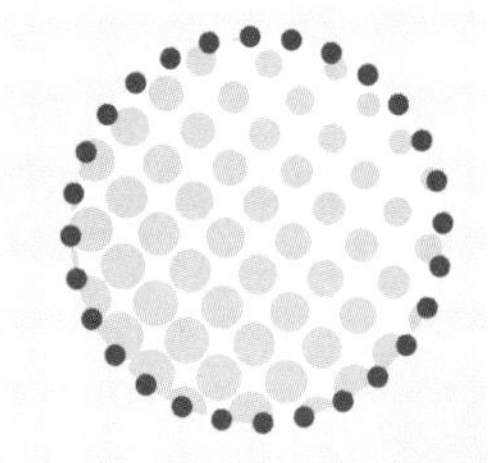

Practice pages

We use commas to separate items in a list.

Rules for punctuating direct speech:

Inverted commas are written before and after the words spoken.	There is always a comma, a question mark, an exclamation mark or a full stop before the closing speech marks.	A new line is started when a different person speaks.

Rewrite the following passage with the correct punctuation.

what time is it asked mario its about six o clock replied jess we need to get ready to go said mario what time is the show asked jess it starts at half past seven replied mario we need to get to the theatre at about seven o clock said jess thatll give us time to get some sweets said mario lets hope its a good show added jess it will be said mario

Brodie's Brain Booster

When we are writing direct speech, we use verbs such as **said**, **asked**, **replied**, **shouted**, **mumbled**, **whispered**. Can you think of more speech verbs?

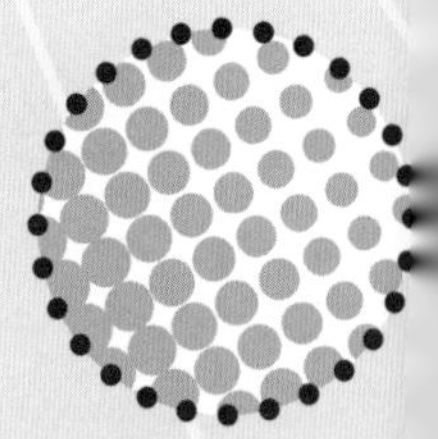

Commas are often used after introductory phrases.

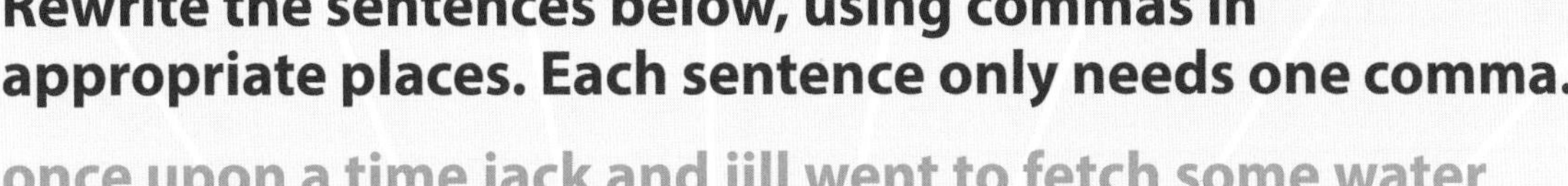

Rewrite the sentences below, using commas in appropriate places. Each sentence only needs one comma.

once upon a time jack and jill went to fetch some water

before the show started mario and jess bought some sweets

when mum collected the car she noticed it was very dirty

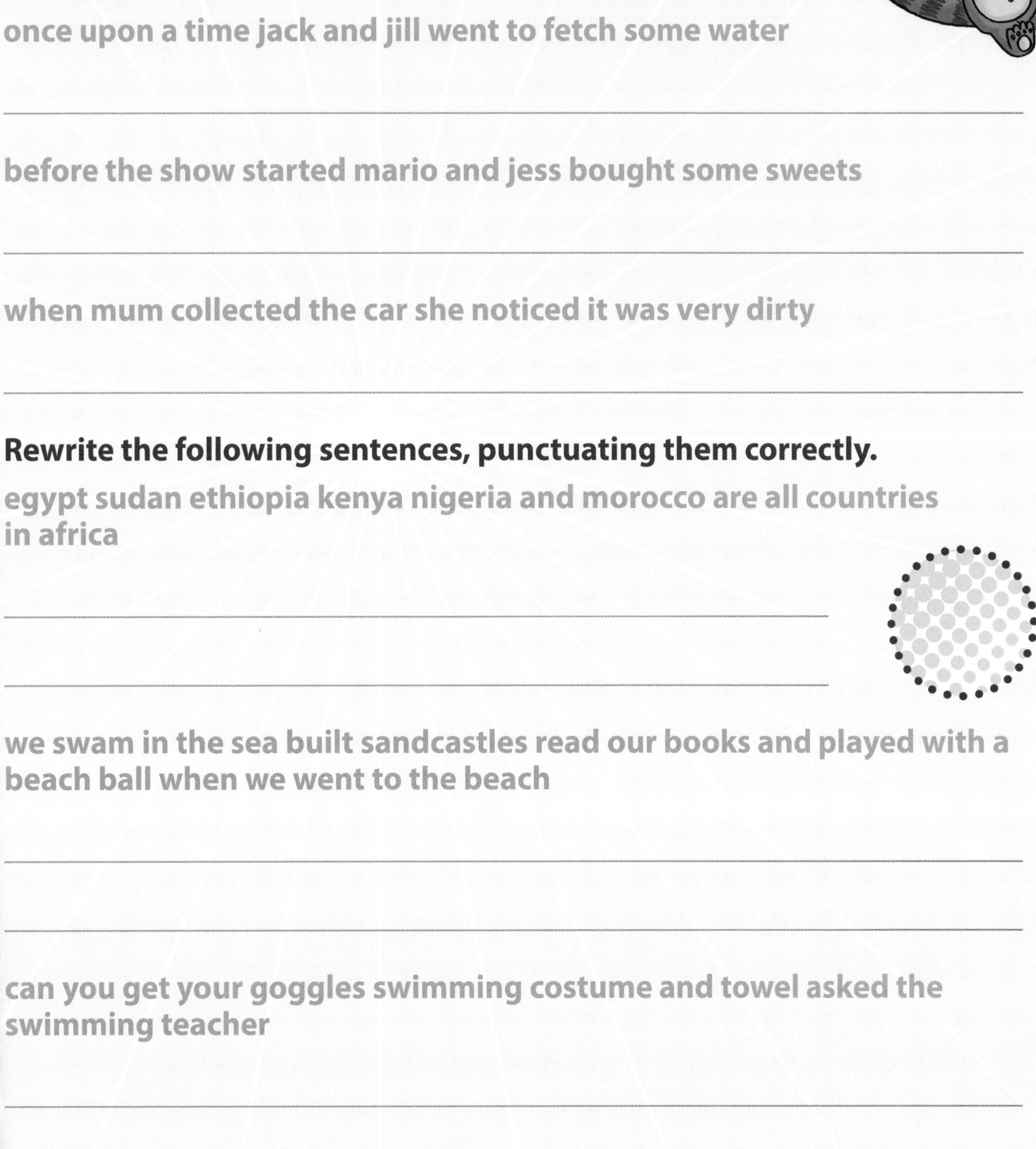

Rewrite the following sentences, punctuating them correctly.

egypt sudan ethiopia kenya nigeria and morocco are all countries in africa

we swam in the sea built sandcastles read our books and played with a beach ball when we went to the beach

can you get your goggles swimming costume and towel asked the swimming teacher

Practice pages

Rewrite the sentences below, using commas, brackets or dashes where appropriate.

The door opened suddenly and there was the prince.

I heard the phone ringing the one in the kitchen so I put down my book.

I rushed to answer the phone nobody there.

The evening meal delicious though it was took too long to prepare.

We need to act quickly this is an emergency

Under the sea down below the level we can swim to there is a wide range of wildlife.

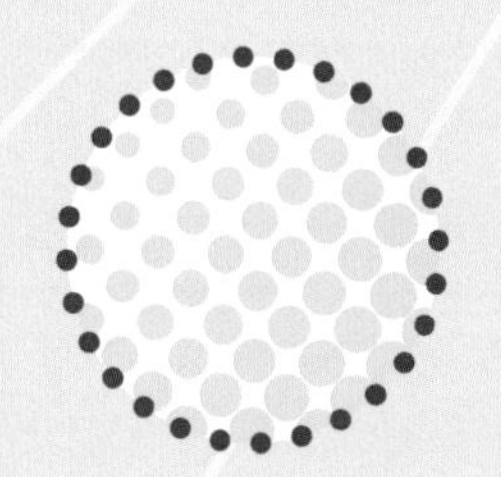

Brodie's Brain Booster
Write down a conversation that you have had today.

Write the following conversation out correctly.

what do you want to do this afternoon asked alisha i would like to go to the cinema replied joe what film is on said alisha i dont know could be anything said joe i dont think i want to go then said alisha can we go swimming asked joe no i havent got my swimming costume here replied alisha what would you like to do asked joe shall we just stay in and watch a film asked alisha thats a good idea fantastic said joe

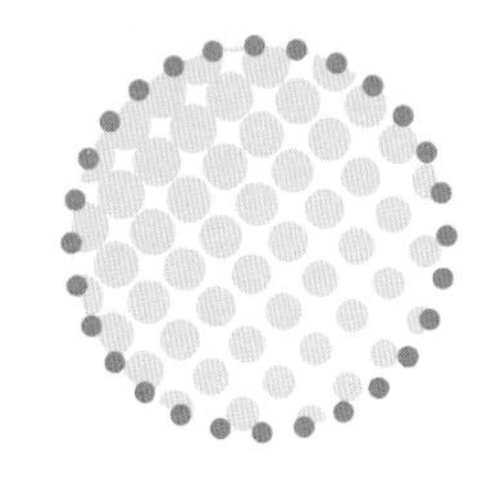

ANSWERS

Use the answers to check your child's progress but also to give prompts and ideas if they are needed. Note that sometimes your child's answer may not match the answer given here but could be just as good!

The audience went quiet when the curtains opened.

Suddenly the first actor appeared in a puff of smoke.

Everyone clapped loudly, even though she had not said a word.

There was great surprise when she started singing.

The song ended with an extremely high note.

The audience leapt to their feet in great excitement.

Brain Booster:

Your child could list names, places, days, months, titles.

My aunt has done a lot of travelling this year.

She went to France in February and China in March.

She was at home for Easter but then went to America in May.

She visited my Uncle William in June.

She told me that she watched a film called Moana when she was on the plane.

I am glad she is at home now but on Monday she is going to Germany until Friday.

What is the highest mountain in the world?

The highest mountain in the world is Mount Everest.

What is the biggest ocean in the world?

The biggest ocean is the Pacific Ocean.

What is the longest river in the world?

Some people think that the longest river in the world is the Amazon River and some people think it is the River Nile.

Brain Booster:

Help your child to find information about the world's longest rivers.

Check your child's questions.

Brain Booster:

Help your child to find information about rivers and lakes in your local area.

Check your child's answers.

Brain Booster:

Help your child to identify a special place.

What time is the bus coming ✓

How many days are there until Christmas ✓

Where is the remote control ✓

What would you like for your birthday ✓

When are you going on holiday ✓

Why did the chicken cross the road ✓

Brain Booster:

An exclamation mark.

Progress Test 1

Where did you go at the weekend?

I went to London and took a boat ride on the River Thames.

When are you going there again?

We hope to go back in October.

I am going to London on Wednesday to see a show.

What show are you going to see?

School of Rock.

What is the longest river in the world ✓

What a great day for a swim!

How scary that film was!

What a mess the dog has made!

I am so excited!

This tastes delicious!

Brain Booster:

Help your child to find exclamations.

p12

didn't

weren't

haven't

should've

what's

can't

Brain Booster:

Omission means something is missed out. Contracted means something has been shortened.

p13

would have

could not

did not

was not

does not

will not

cannot

it is

p14

The dog's lead is hanging on the hook.

I was surprised how long the mouse's tail was.

I picked up Amy's book when she dropped it on the floor.

She told me it was Ted's book not hers.

I put the book on Ted's desk.

Brain Booster:

Help your child to spot possessive apostrophes in use.

p15

The women's choir performed at the Royal Albert Hall.

Maria and Luke went to the children's party.

The girls' football team won the whole tournament.

The boys' football team came second.

p16

The ladies' netball teams were ready for the tournament. ✓

Check your child's sentences.

Progress Test 2

My mum's car is bright yellow but the seats are blue. ✓

The dog's blanket fell on the floor.

I watched Amy's paper aeroplane as it flew across the playground.

All the other children's aeroplanes didn't get very far.

Some of the animals' cages are brightly coloured.

We added an extra tunnel to our hamster's cage.

p18

"That is not what I meant," said Mum.

"I would really like a bar of chocolate," said Tom.

"So would I," said Mum.

Brain Booster:

Help your child to find inverted commas.

p19

"When will my new book arrive?" asked Ted.

"It should come today," replied Lucy.

"Thank you for ordering it for me," said Ted.

"Well it is your birthday," said Lucy.

p20

Ideas include: answered, whispered, repeated, muttered, responded, yelled, called, admitted, agreed

"Do you want to play football?" asked Molly.

"That would be good but we can't," said Elliott.

"Why not?" said Molly.

"Because we haven't got a ball," answered Elliott.

p21

Check that your child has continued the script appropriately.

p22

Check your child's direct speech.

Brain Booster:

Help your child to find speech where no speech verb or speaker is shown. Can you both work out who is speaking?

p23

"What is your favourite flavour?" asked Karen.

"I think it's vanilla," replied Oliver.

"Mine is mint choc chip," said Karen.

"I don't like that one," said Oliver.

"The one I don't like is fudge," said Karen.

"Why not?" asked Oliver.

"It's too sweet."

Progress Test 3

"This maths is easy," said Claire.

"It may be for you but I'm finding it quite difficult," replied Harley.

"Can I help you?" asked Claire.

"Can you show me how to change this fraction to a decimal?" asked Harley.

"You know that a half is the same as five tenths, don't you?" asked Claire.

"So a half must be zero point five!" exclaimed Harley.

'Can you play a musical instrument?" asked Molly.

I can play the guitar," replied Fynn.

I can play the piano," said Molly.

We could play a duet," said Fynn.

What song do you want to play?" asked Molly.

You choose."

25

'he first sentence implies that George is going o be eaten!

lum was asking George if he was ready to eat.

3rain Booster:

lelp your child to find commas.

p26

Once upon a time, the Duke of York climbed up a hill.

Early this morning, the weather was quite good.

Before we start, would you like a cup of tea?

At that moment, the sun appeared from behind a cloud.

After the rain, the grass looked fresh and green.

Next month, I am going to start rugby lessons.

p27

We bought new trousers, socks, shirts and jackets ready for our winter holiday.

My mum has been to France, Spain, Portugal, Italy and Germany for her work.

There are lots of oak trees in the forest but there are also some beech, ash, birch and sycamore trees.

The teacher said I should have pens, pencils, an eraser, a pencil sharpener and a protractor in my pencil case.

p28

The bike shop, the one near the railway station, sells a bike in every colour.

I forgot my book, which I only got yesterday, so I had to go back for it.

The tent, a green one, was big enough to make a huge den.

We caught the train at Victoria, which is our most convenient station, and reached the seaside in less than an hour and a half.

p29

Check that your child has added appropriate information to each sentence. Here are some examples:

I got off my bike and went into the shop, the one next to the hairdressers, to buy some sweets.

The ferocious cat, a large tabby, chased off the angry dog.

After the show, if there's enough time, we can stay for a while and have a chat.

The plates, our best ones, clattered to the floor and smashed into hundreds of pieces.

Brain Booster:

Help your child search for bracketing commas.

p30

Check the addresses.

Progress Test 4

"I'm stuck on my maths so I'm going to ask, Poppy," said Joe. ✓

After going for a swim, we had a boat trip to the island. ✓

The new house, built last year, can be described as an eco-house. ✓

p32

Check your child's sentence.

Brain Booster:

Help your child to search for brackets.

p33

The tree house – high above the ground – gave a great vantage point to see who was approaching.

The superhero – travelling faster than the speed of sound – shot across the night sky.

Check your child's sentence.

Brain Booster:

Help your child to search for pairs of dashes.

p34

I was thrilled when the experiment was successful – hooray!

Be careful of that tree – I've just planted it.

Put the television on – my friend is starring in a new show.

Hurry up and get the tomato ketchup – my chips are getting cold.

p35

We parked our scooters at the bottom of the hill – a very handy spot.

Brain Booster:

Help your child to search for dashes used to miss out words.

p36

Check that your child has written the conversation correctly.

Brain Booster:

The rules are shown on page 19.

p37

Your child can choose to use commas, brackets or dashes. Here are some suggested answers:

It was raining pouring down, so we left the beach early.

The book, which was written in 2017, is all about a boy who shrinks.

I went to the bookshop – it had closed early.

The chocolate was delicious – it tasted of raspberries

The school (opened in 1878) is still very important in the village.

The new house – very modern in appearance – has a flat roof.

Progress Test 5

Possible answers:

The sky was bright blue – just a few clouds – and we could feel the warmth from the sun.

I jumped on my bike, which is a mountain bike, and raced to the end of the field.

We ate all the food (delicious) then got back on the trampolines.

The sun shone all day and the sea was warm – a fantastic day at the beach.

The work was much easier than I expected – I'm beginning to like maths.

p39

My mum and I watched a great television programme on Wednesday.

It was all about a desert in Africa.

It is hot there all year round, even in January.

There are lots of different animals there.

They are adapted to cope with the hot conditions.

I told my teacher, Mrs Watkins, all about the programme.

Brain Booster:

Sahara, Kalahari and Namib are the main deserts in Africa.

p40

What is the biggest hot desert in the world?

The biggest hot desert in the world is the Sahara Desert.

Where is the Sahara Desert?

The Sahara Desert is in North Africa.

What is the biggest cold desert in the world?

The biggest cold desert is Antarctica.

Brain Booster:

Help your child to find the information.

p41

Dad can't find his phone so he's using Mum's.

I found Rob's book which he'd left in the childminder's car.

I would've liked to call Olivia yesterday but she was away.

I haven't seen Holly's latest picture but I know it'll be good because she's a great artist.

It takes a long time to cut the lawn as the garden's so big.

We've brought lots of children's toys for the toddlers to play with.

p42

"What time is it?" asked Mario.

"It's about six o'clock," replied Jess.

"We need to get ready to go," said Mario.

"What time is the show?" asked Jess.

"It starts at half past seven," replied Mario.

"We need to get to the theatre at about seven o'clock," said Jess.

"That'll give us time to get some sweets," said Mario.

"Let's hope it's a good show," added Jess.

"It will be," said Mario.

Brain Booster:

Your child could look back at page 20.

p43

Once upon a time, Jack and Jill went to fetch some water.

Before the show started, Mario and Jess bought some sweets.

When mum collected the car, she noticed it was very dirty.

Egypt, Sudan, Ethiopia, Kenya, Nigeria and Morocco are all countries in Africa.

We swam in the sea, built sandcastles, read our books and played with a beach ball when we went to the beach.

"Can you get your goggles, swimming costume and towel?" asked the swimming teacher.

p44

The door opened suddenly – there was the prince.

I heard the phone ringing, the one in the kitchen, so I put down my book.

I rushed to answer the phone – nobody there.

The evening meal, delicious though it was, took too long to prepare.

We need to act quickly – this is an emergency!

Under the sea down (below the level we can swim to) there is a wide range of wildlife.

Brain Booster:

Help your child to write a conversation that has happened today.

Progress Test 6

"What do you want to do this afternoon?" asked Alisha.

"I would like to go to the cinema," replied Joe.

"What film is on?" said Alisha.

"I don't know, could be anything," said Joe.

"I don't think I want to go then," said Alisha.

"Can we go swimming?" asked Joe.

"No, I haven't got my swimming costume here," replied Alisha.

"What would you like to do?" asked Joe.

"Shall we just stay in and watch a film?" asked Alisha.

"That's a good idea – fantastic!" said Joe.